Summer Solutions.
Minutes a Day–Mastery for a Lifetime!

Pre-K

Language Arts

Joan Archer

Bright Ideas Press, LLC
Beachwood, OH

Summer Solutions
Language Arts Pre-K

Printed in the United States of America

The writers of *Simple Solutions* Language Arts aligned the series in accordance with information from the following:

National Governors Association Center for Best Practices, Council of Chief State School Officers, 2010.

United States coin images from the United States Mint.

ISBN: 978-1-60873-411-5

Cover Design: Dan Mazzola
Lauren Dambrogio
Editor: Lauren Dambrogio

Summer Solutions

Pre-K Language Arts

Reviewed Skills Include:

- Prewriting Skills

- Sorting/Classification Skills

- Color Word Recognition & Color Identification

- Letter Recognition

- Letter Sound Recognition

- Letter Writing

- Sequencing

- Opposites

- Rhyming

- Beginning Letter Sounds

- Syllables

Answers to Lessons begin on page 63.

Lesson #1

1.

1. Help the children fly their kites by tracing the lines.

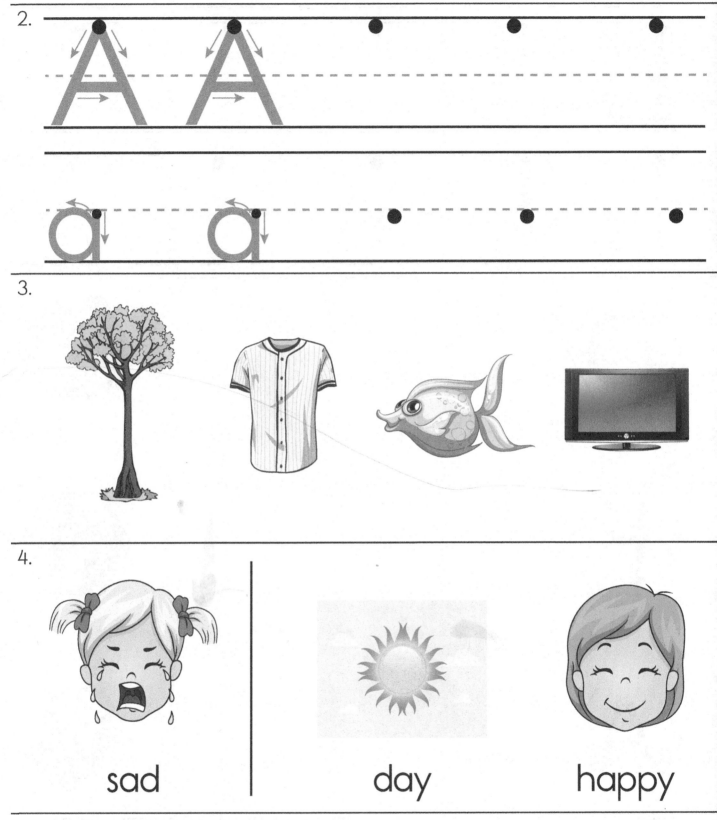

2.

3.

4.

sad | day   happy

2. Trace and write the letters.

3. Circle the non-living things.

4. Circle the picture that shows the opposite of the first one.

Lesson #2

1.

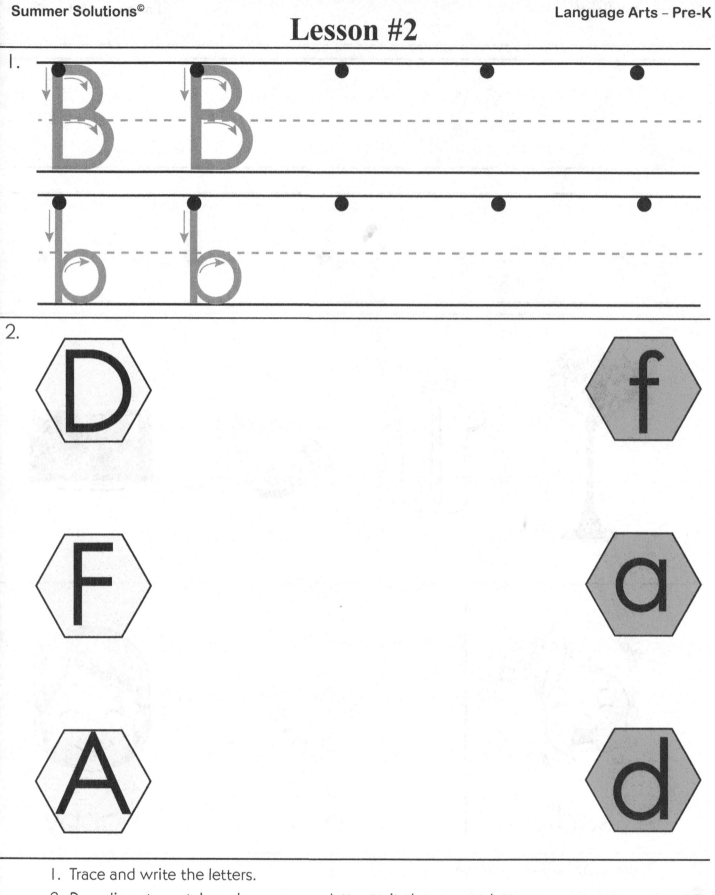

1. Trace and write the letters.
2. Draw lines to match each upper case letter to its lower case letter.

3. Say the name of each picture. Write **Hh** under the picture that begins like *hammer*.

4. Say the name of each picture. Circle the pictures that rhyme.

5. Trace and write the letters.

Lesson #3

1.

2.

3.

t   n   r   z   g   b

1. Say the word *ball*. Clap the number of beats or syllables. Color a circle for each beat that you hear.

2. Circle the picture that happened first.

3. Say the name of each picture. Circle the letter that stands for its beginning sound.

4.

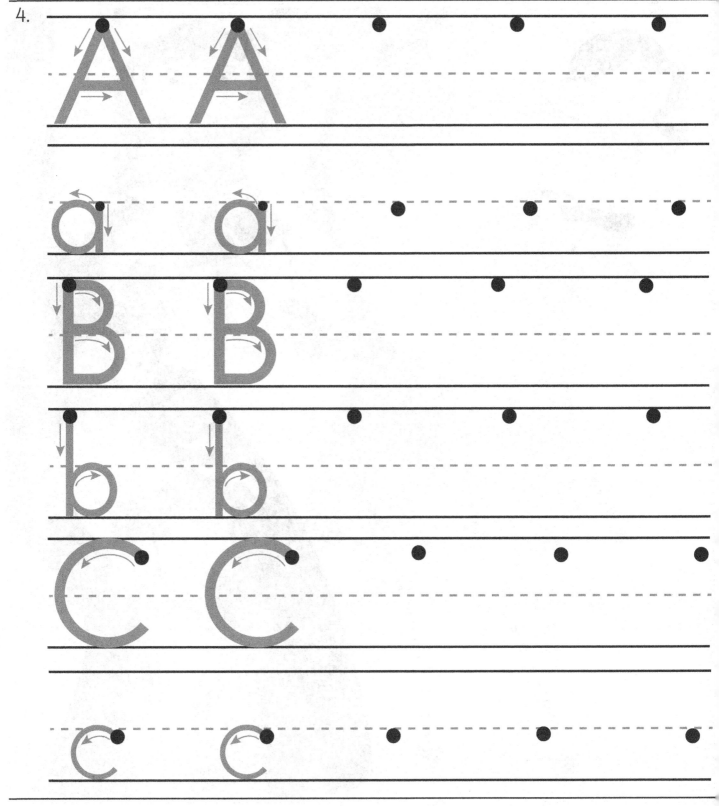

4. Trace and write the letters.

Lesson #4

I.

I. Help the kids go down the slides by tracing the lines.

2. Circle the picture that belongs with the first one.

3. Trace and write the letters.

4. Trace the word *yellow*. Circle the objects that are yellow.

Lesson #5

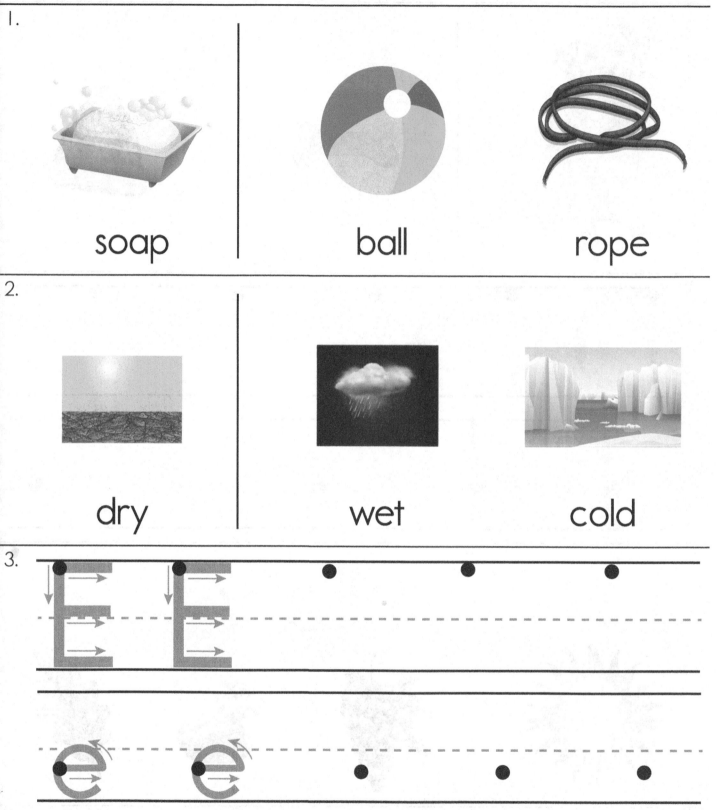

1.

soap   ball   rope

2.

dry   wet   cold

3.

1. Say the name of each picture. Circle the picture whose name rhymes with *soap*.

2. Circle the picture that shows the opposite of the first one.

3. Trace and write the letters.

4.

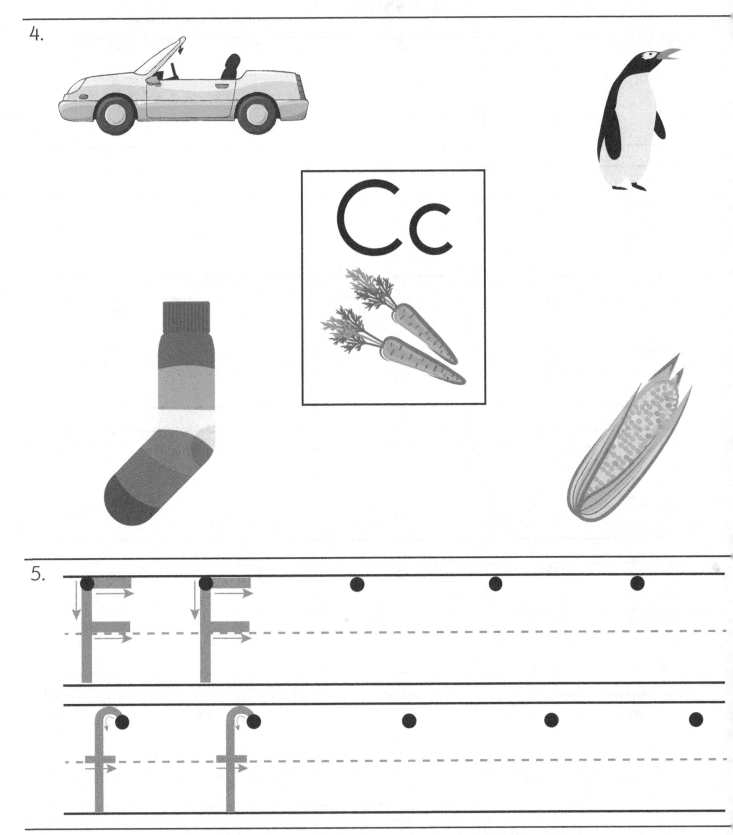

Cc

5.

4. Say the name of each picture. Circle the pictures that begin like *carrot*.

5. Trace and write the letters.

Lesson #6

1.

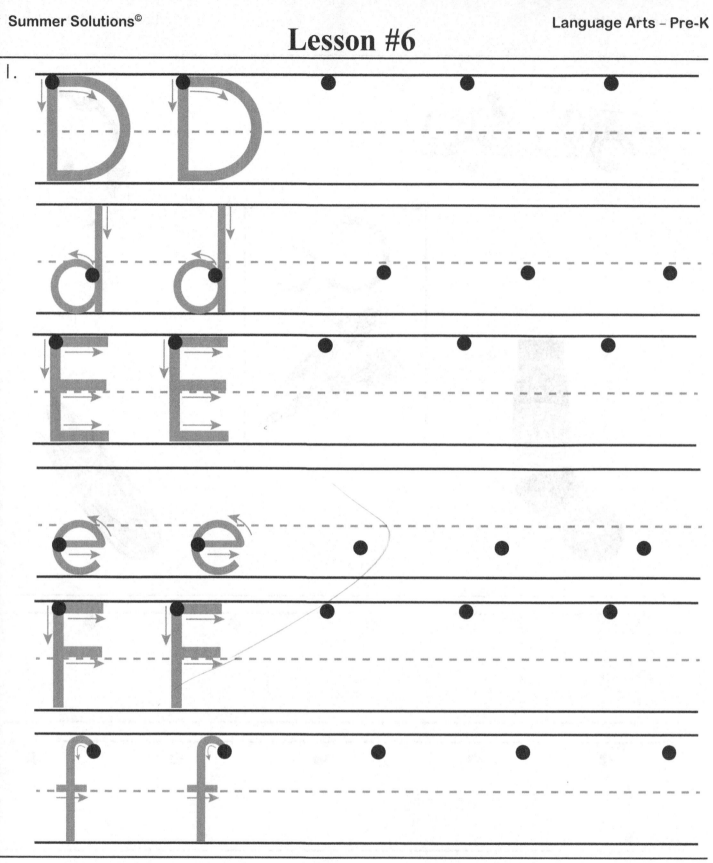

1. Trace and write the letters.

2.

3.

1 2 3 4

2. Connect the dots from A–O. Color the picture.

3. Say the word *dinosaur*. Clap the number of syllables. Circle the number of syllables.

Lesson #7

1.

1. Circle four objects that do not belong.

2.

G G

g g

3.

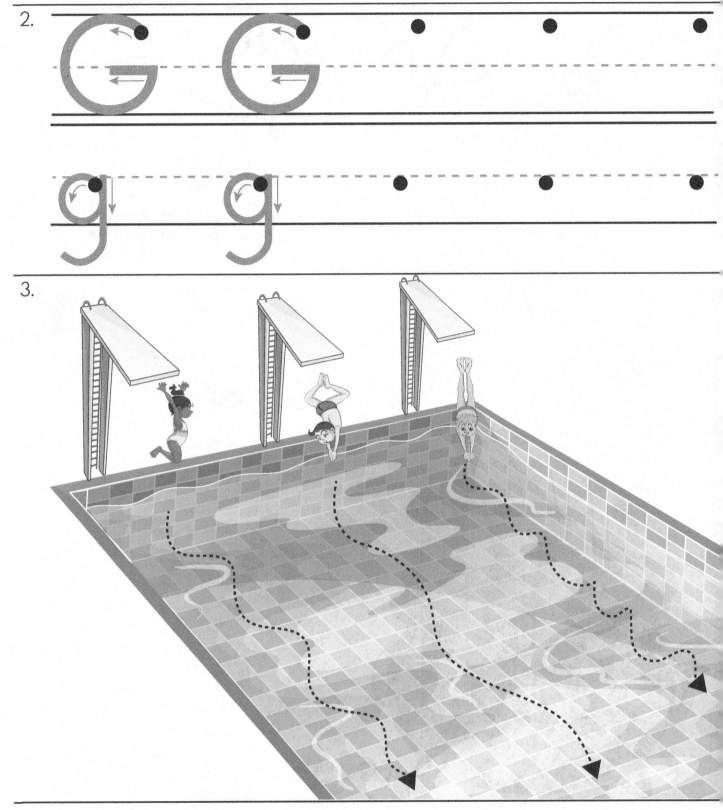

2. Trace and write the letters.

3. Help the kids get into the pool by tracing the lines.

Lesson #8

1.

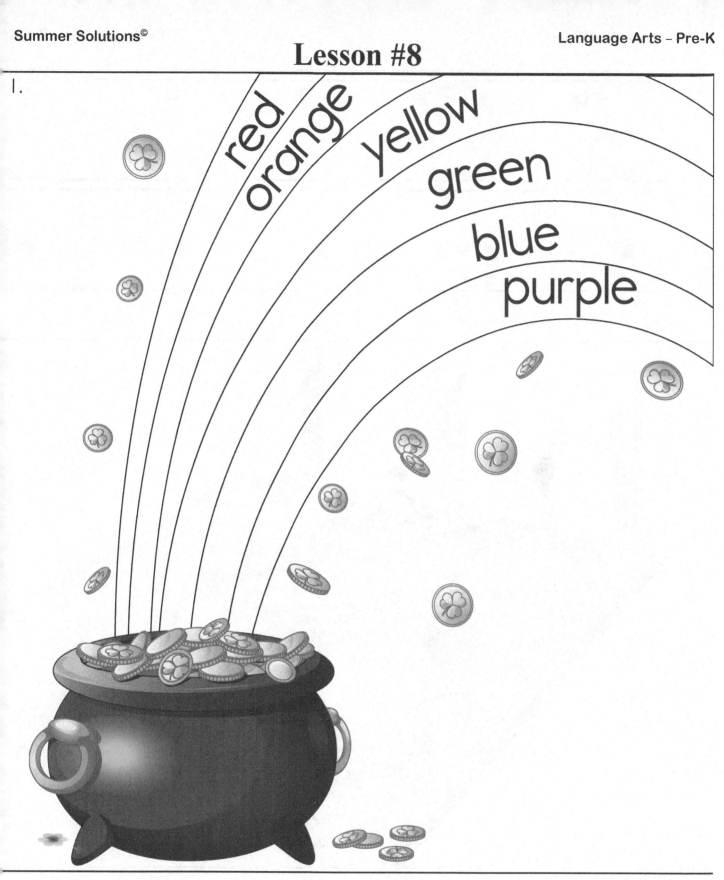

red
orange
yellow
green
blue
purple

1. Read the color words. Color the rainbow.

2.

3.

4.

2. Say the name of each picture. Write **Rr** under the picture that begins like *rooster*.

3. Look at the first picture. Circle the picture that comes next.

4. Trace and write the letters.

Lesson #9

1.

big   small   soft

2.

3.

a   h   d   s   f   l

1. Circle the picture that shows the opposite of the first one.
2. Say the name of each picture. Circle the pictures that rhyme.
3. Say the name of each picture. Circle the letter that stands for its beginning sound.

4.

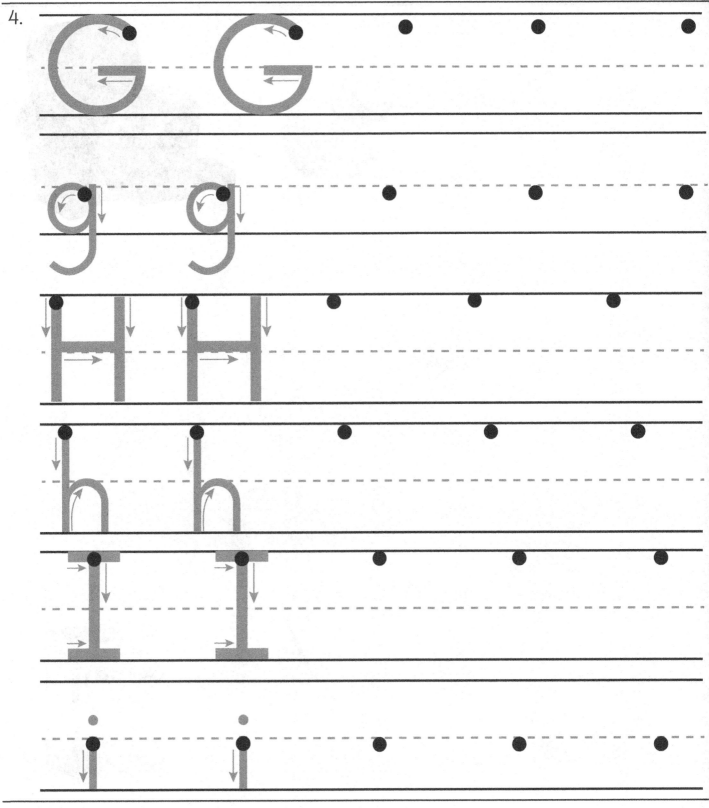

4. Trace and write the letters.

Lesson #10

I.

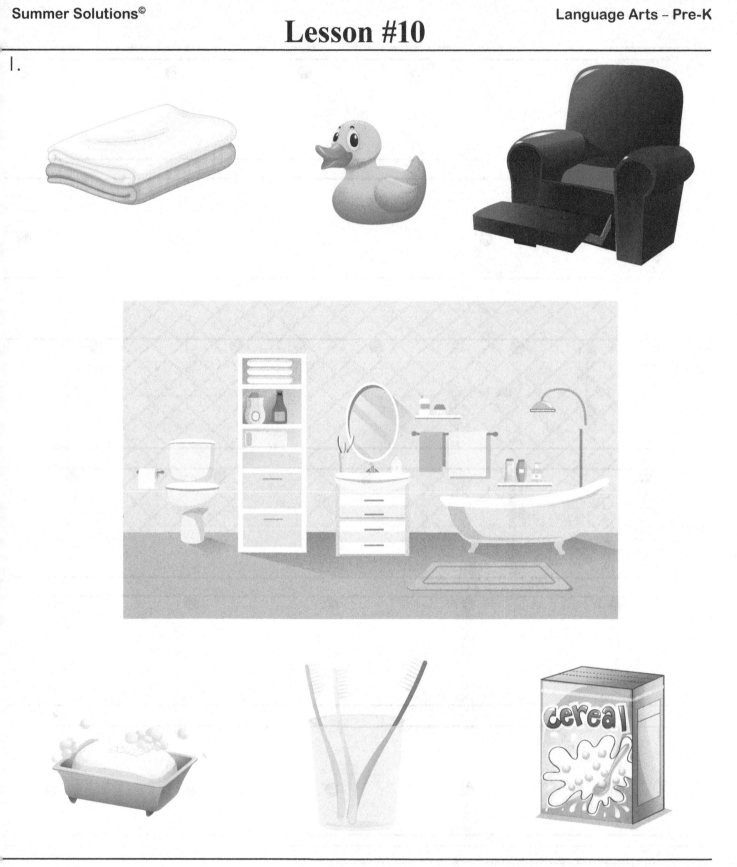

1. Circle the objects that belong in a bathroom.

2.

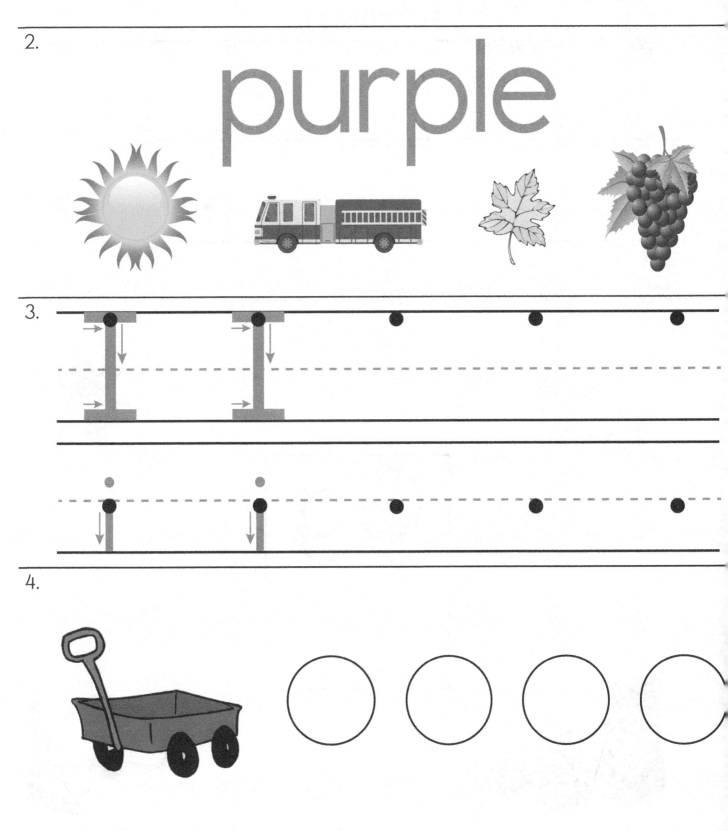

3.

4.

2. Trace the word *purple*. Circle the objects that are purple.

3. Trace and write the letters.

4. Say the word *wagon*. Clap the number of beats. Color a circle for each beat that you hear.

Lesson #11

1.

2.

1. Trace and write the letters.
2. Say the name of each picture. Circle the pictures that begin like *goat*.

3.

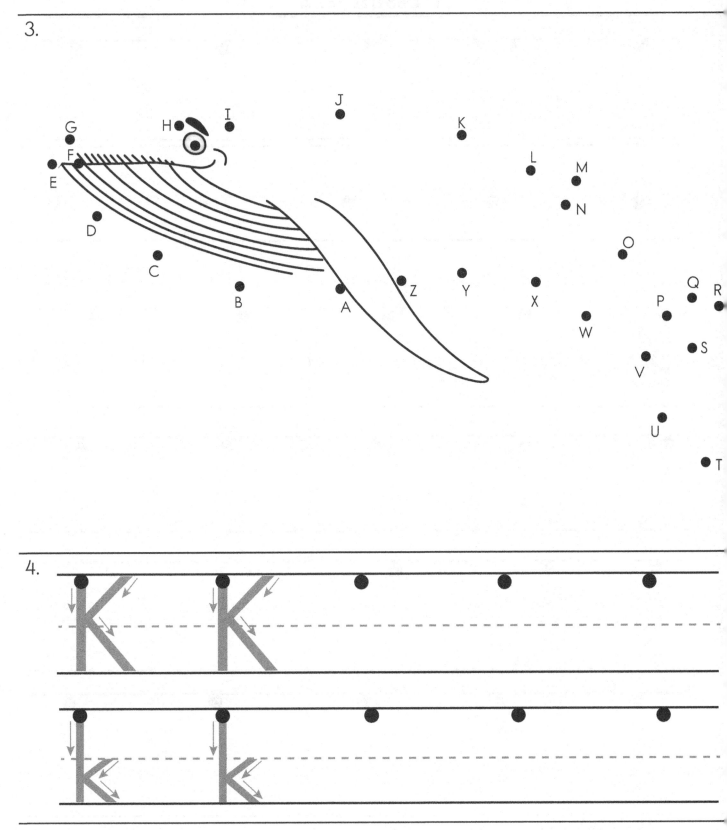

4.

3. Connect the dots from A–Z. Color the picture.

4. Trace and write the letters.

Lesson #12

1.

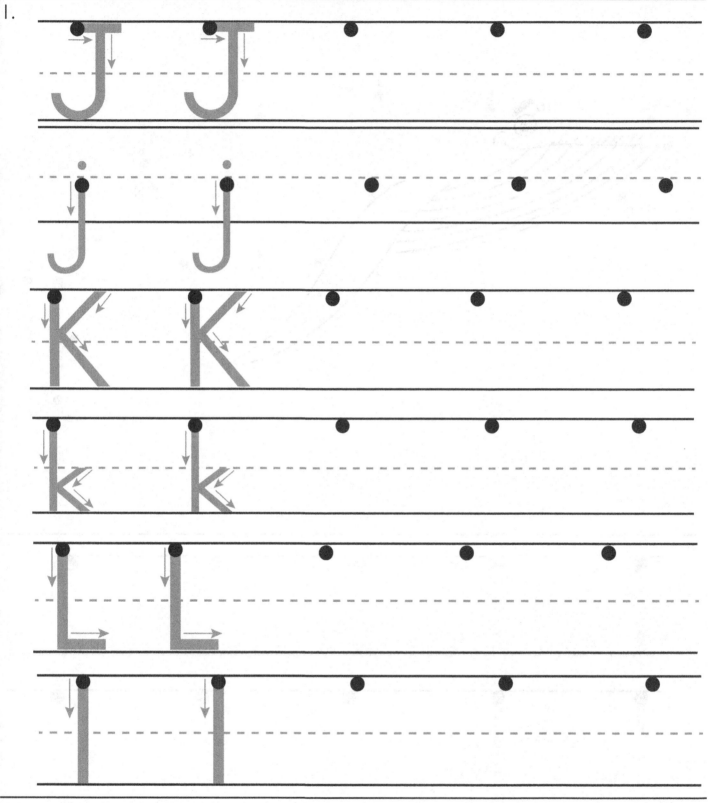

1. Trace and write the letters.

2. Circle the picture that happened last.

3. Circle the things that fly.

4. Say the name of each picture. Circle the picture whose name rhymes with *flag*.

Lesson #13

1.

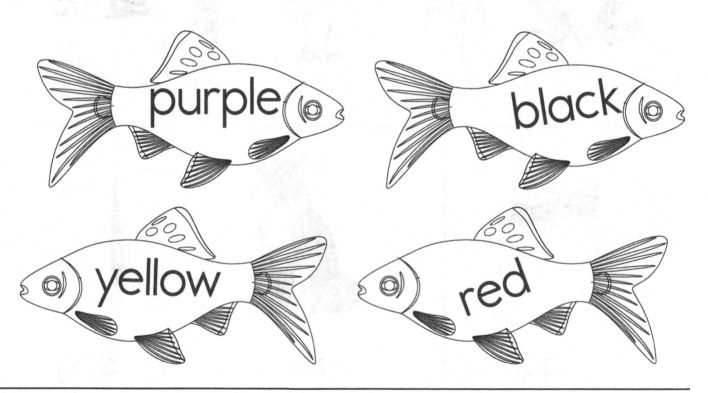

1. Read the color words. Color the fish.

2.

t　　h　　f　|　u　　p　　d

3.

old　|　hot　　young

4.

2. Say the name of each picture. Circle the letter that stands for its beginning sound.

3. Circle the picture that shows the opposite of the first one.

4. Trace and write the letters.

Lesson #14

1.

2.

1. Say the name of each picture. Circle the pictures that begin like *moon*.

2. Trace and write the letters.

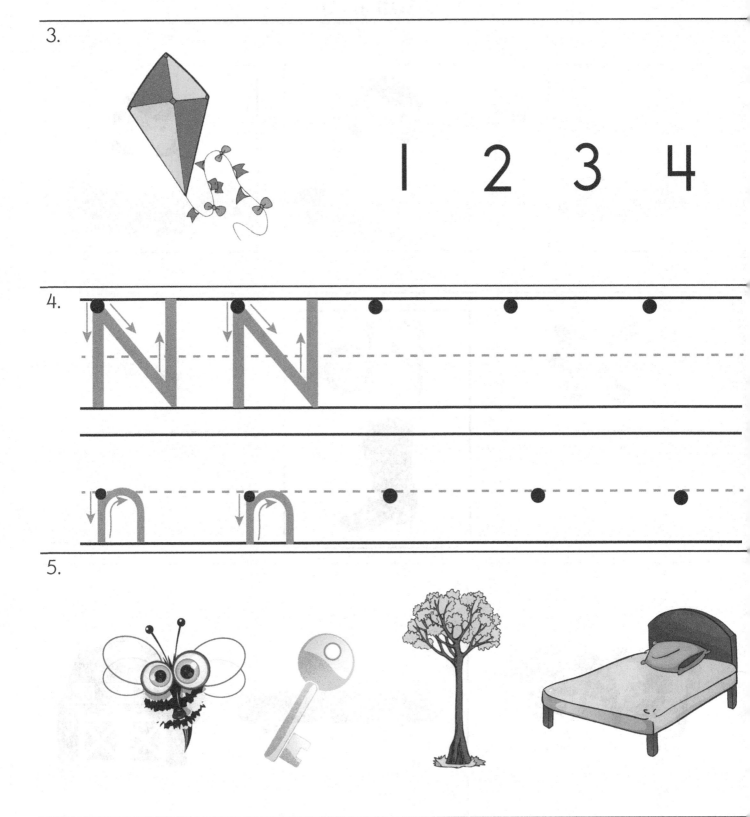

3.   1   2   3   4

4.

5.

3. Say the word *kite*. Clap the number of beats or syllables. Circle the number of syllables.

4. Trace and write the letters.

5. Say the name of each picture. Circle the pictures that rhyme.

Lesson #15

1.

2.

3.

1. Look at the first picture. Circle the picture that comes next.

2. Say the name of each picture. Write **Bb** under the picture that begins like *boot*.

3. Circle the picture that belongs with the first one.

4.

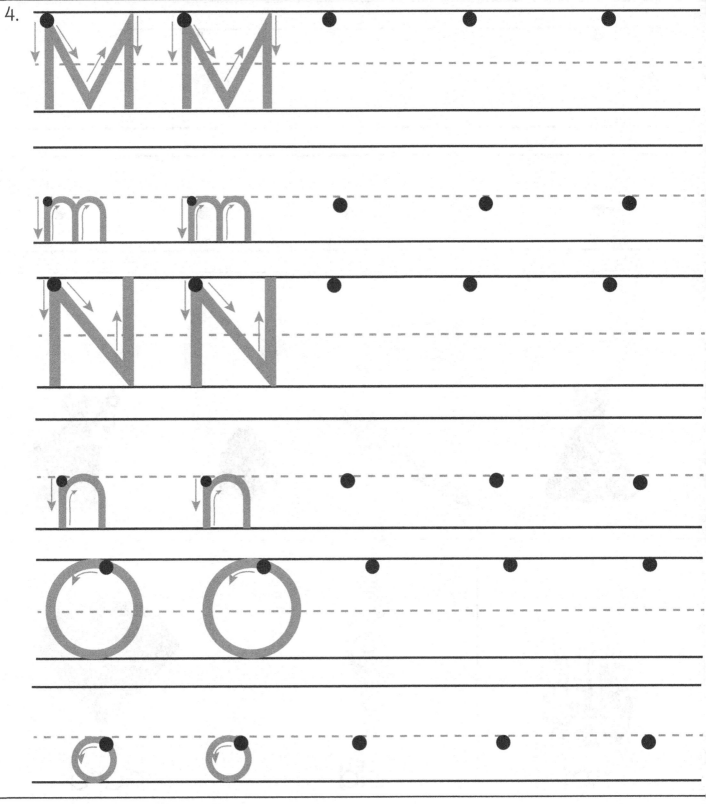

4. Trace and write the letters.

Lesson #16

1.

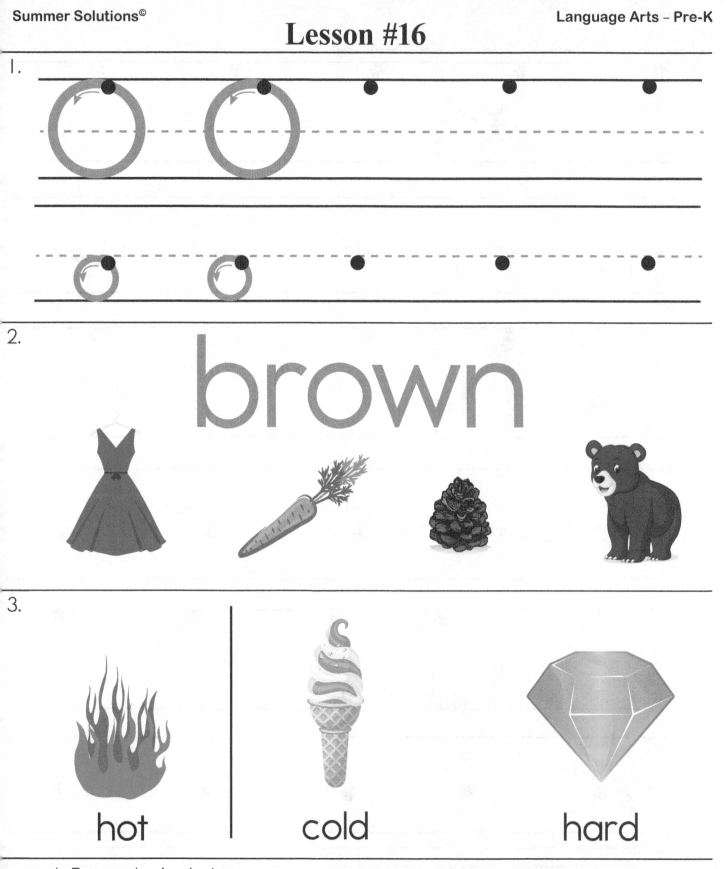

2.

brown

3.

hot | cold   hard

1. Trace and write the letters.
2. Trace the word *brown*. Circle the objects that are brown.
3. Circle the picture that shows the opposite of the first one.

4.

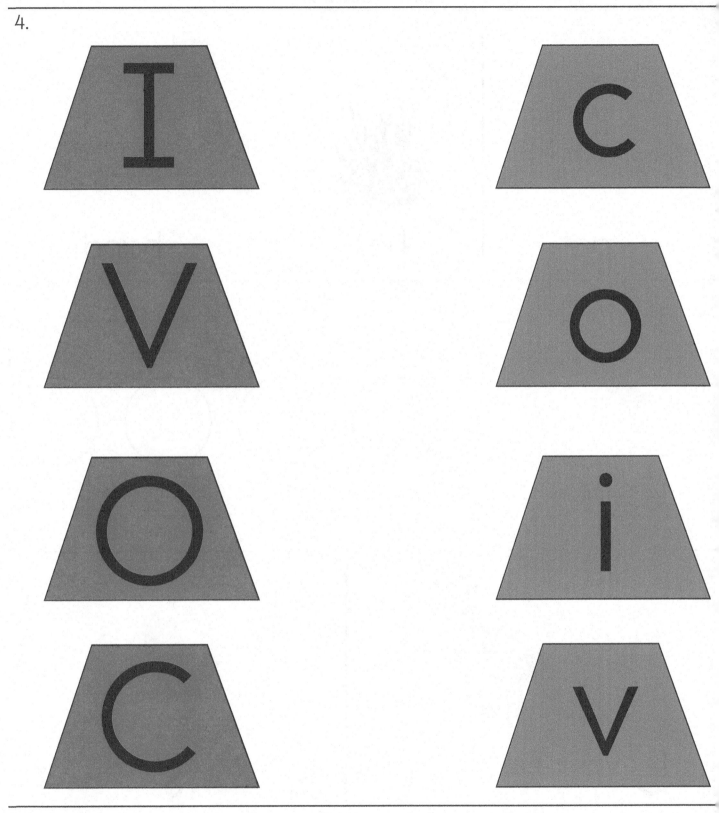

4. Draw a line to match each upper case letter to its lower case letter.

Lesson #17

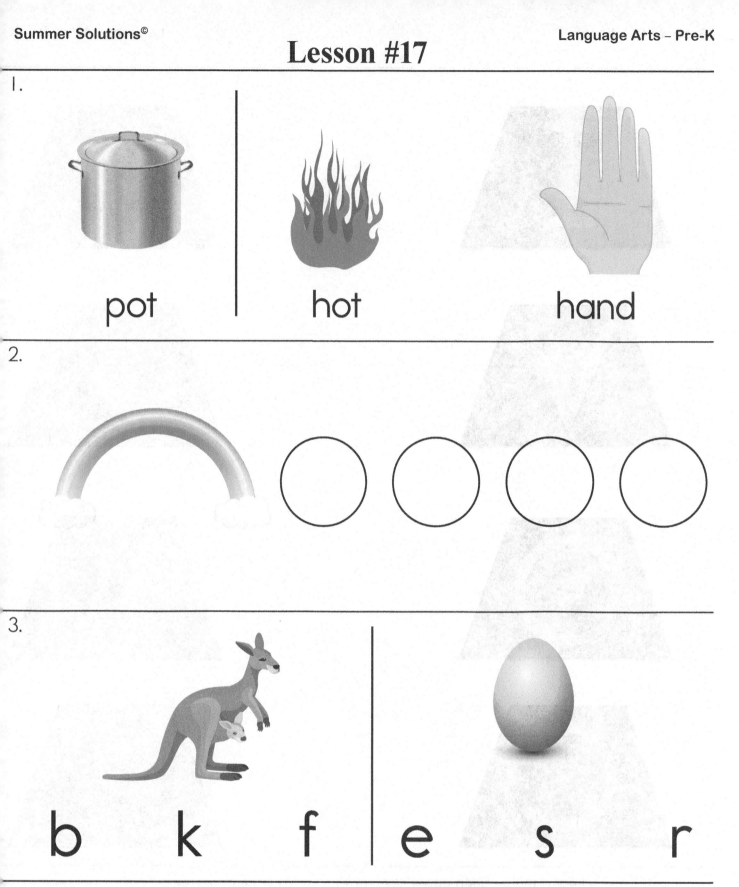

1.

| pot | hot | hand |

2.

3.

b   k   f   e   s   r

1. Say the name of each picture. Circle the picture whose name rhymes with *pot*.

2. Say the word *rainbow*. Clap the number of beats or syllables. Color a circle for each beat that you hear.

3. Say the name of each picture. Circle the letter that stands for its beginning sound.

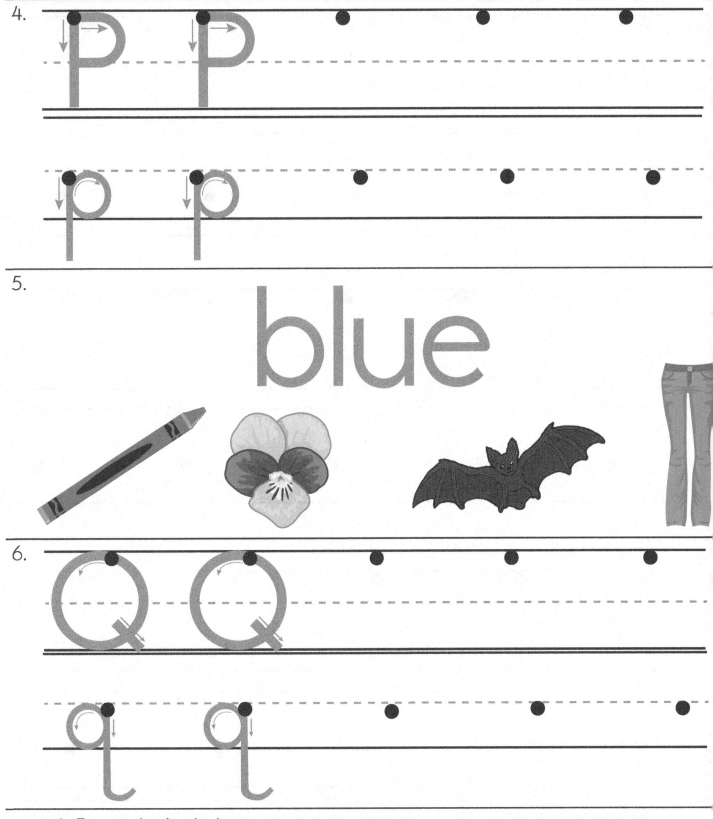

4. Trace and write the letters.

5. Trace the word *blue*. Circle the objects that are blue.

6. Trace and write the letters.

Lesson #18

1.

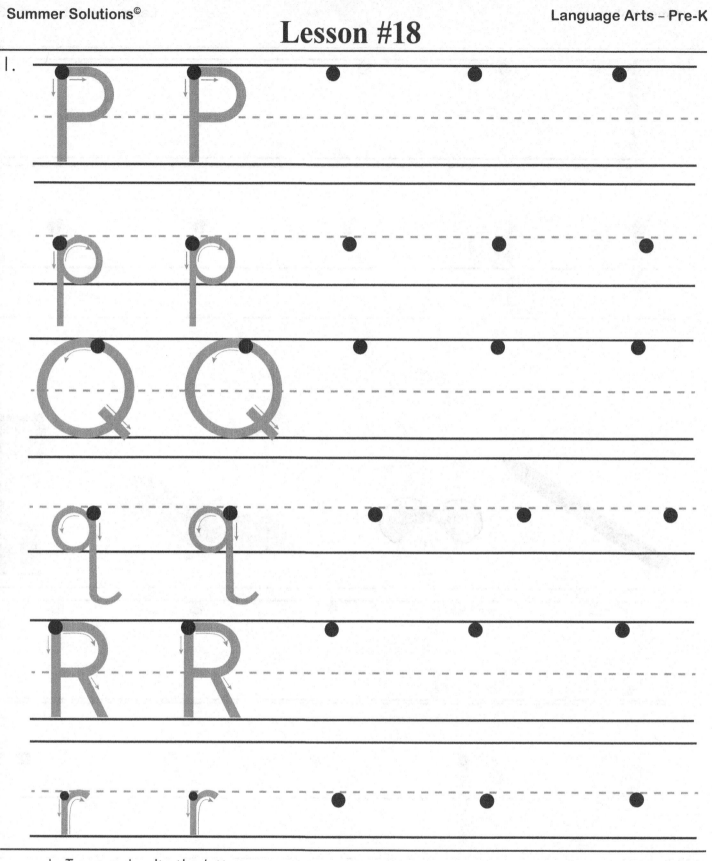

1. Trace and write the letters.

2.

3.

2. Circle the things that have only two legs.

3. Draw a line to match each upper case letter to its lower case letter.

Lesson #19

1. Circle the picture that happened first.

2. Say the name of each picture. Write **Tt** under the picture that begins like *turkey*.

3. Trace and write the letters.

4.

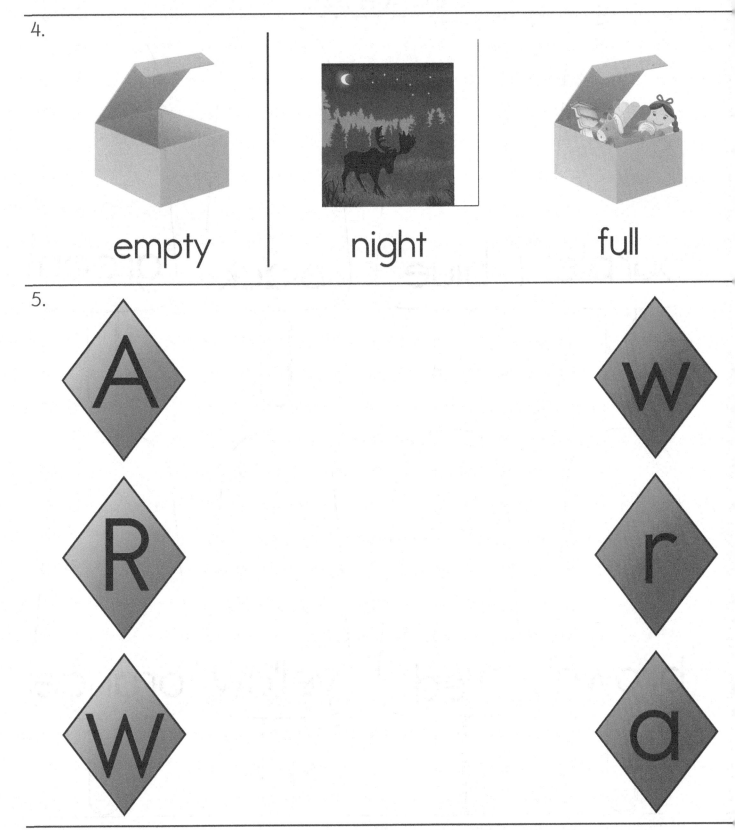

empty   night   full

5.

4. Circle the picture that shows the opposite of the first one.

5. Draw a line to match each upper case letter to its lower case letter.

Lesson #20

1.

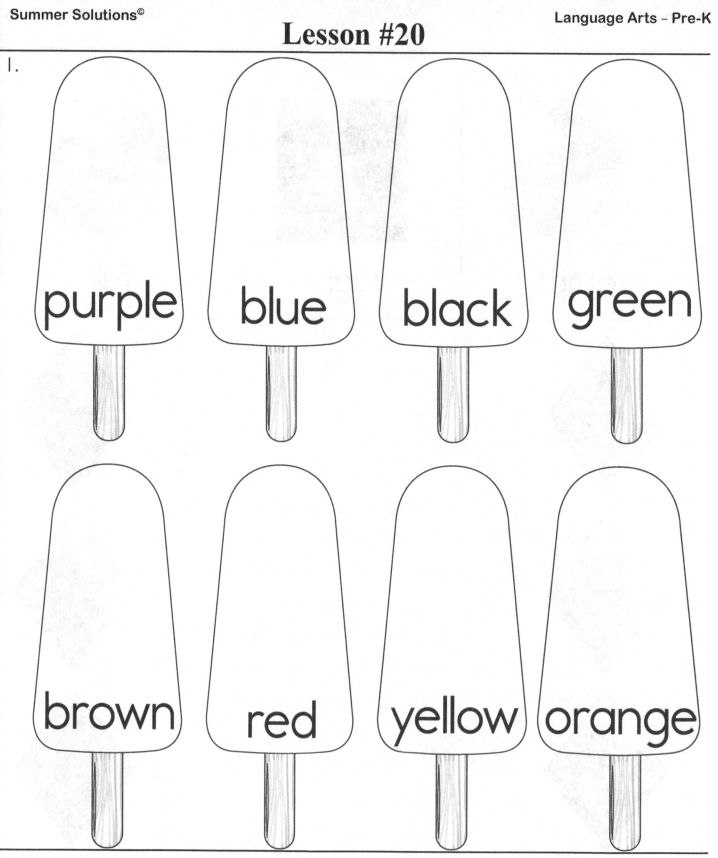

1. Read the color words. Color the popsicles.

2.

3.

4.

2. Trace and write the letters.

3. Say the word *flamingo*. Clap the number of beats or syllables. Color a circle for each beat that you hear.

4. Say the name of each picture. Circle the pictures that rhyme.

Lesson #21

1.

p   t   g | i   s   r

2.

1. Say the name of each picture. Circle the letter that stands for its beginning sound.
2. Connect the dots from A–W. Color the picture.

3.

3. Trace and write the letters.

Lesson #22

1.

1. Circle four objects that do not belong.

2. Say the name of each picture. Write **Ww** under the picture that begins like *watermelon*.

3. Trace the word *black*. Circle the objects that are black.

4. Trace and write the letters.

Lesson #23

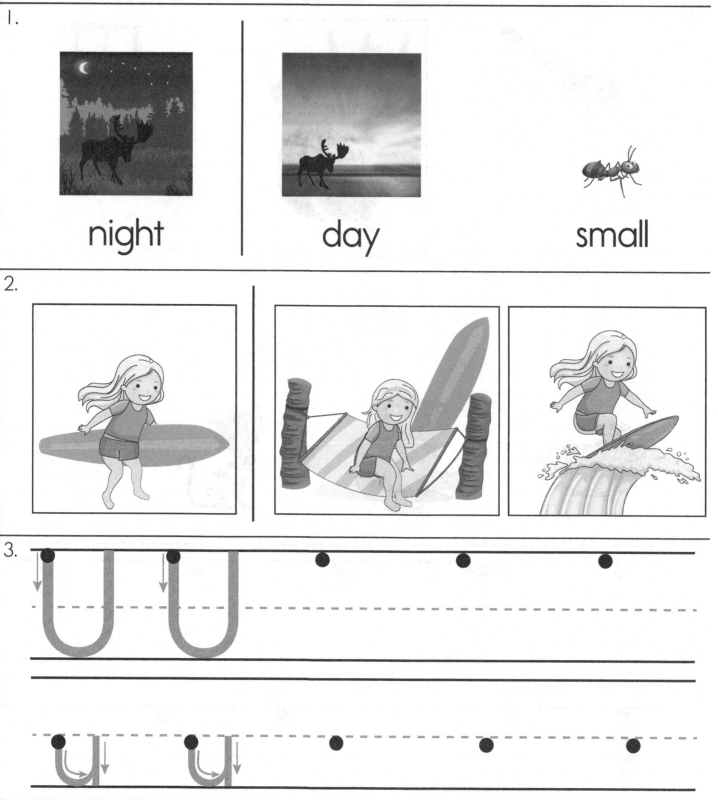

1.

night | day | small

2.

3.

1. Circle the picture that shows the opposite of the first one.

2. Look at the first picture. Circle the picture that comes next.

3. Trace and write the letters.

4.

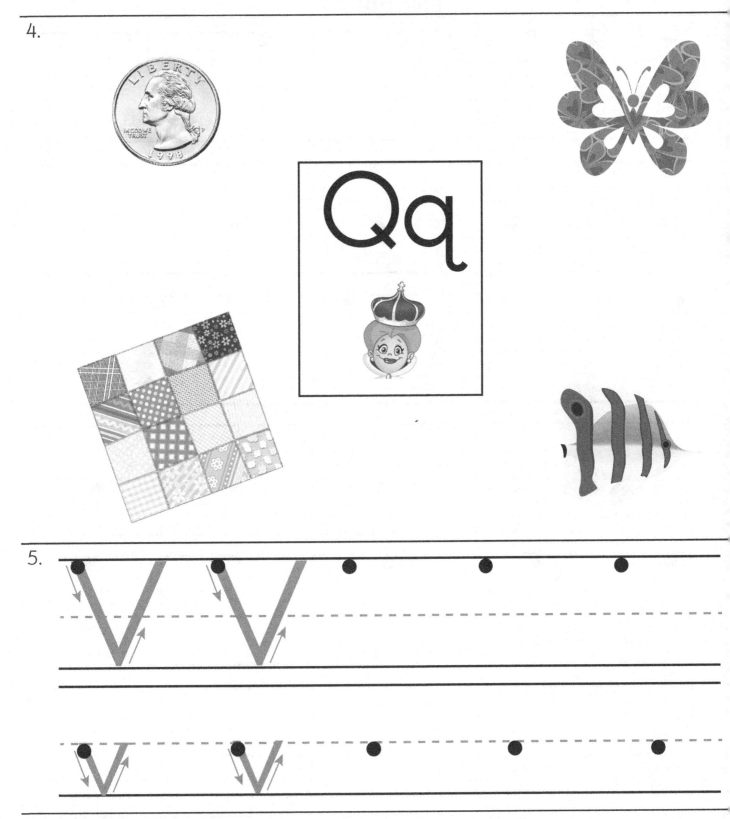

5.

4. Say the name of each picture. Circle the pictures that begin like *queen*.

5. Trace and write the letters.

Lesson #24

1.

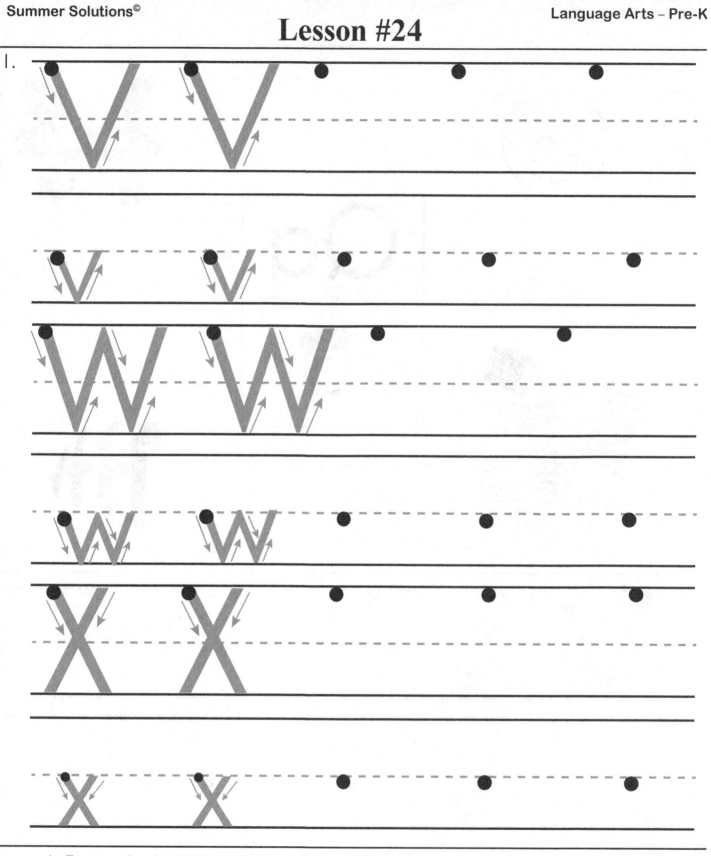

1. Trace and write the letters.

2.

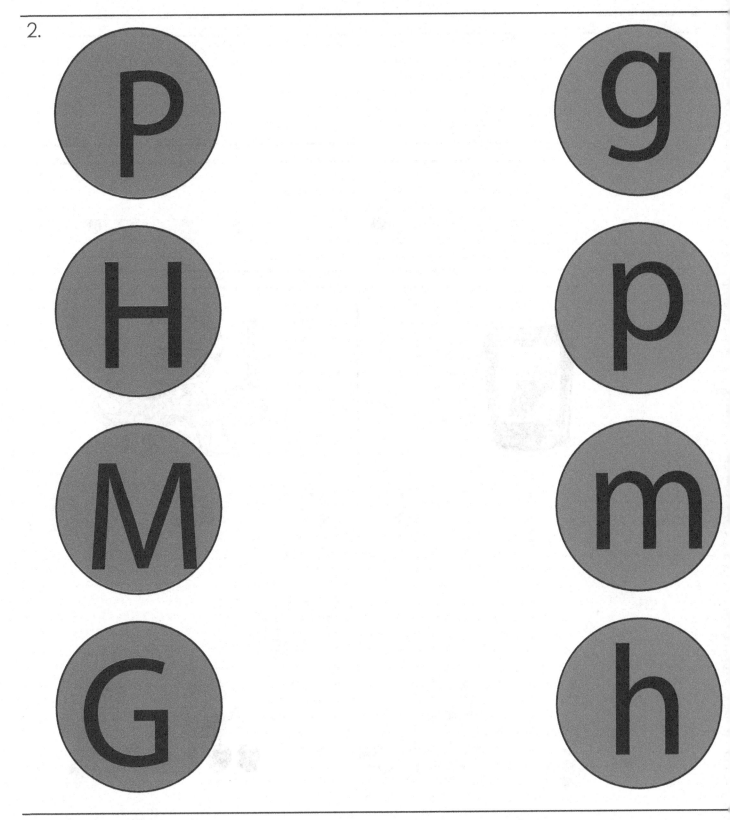

2. Draw a line to match each upper case letter to its lower case letter.

Lesson #25

1.

2.

k   j   s | r   o   m

3.

orange

1. Trace and write the letters.
2. Say the name of each picture. Circle the letter that stands for its beginning sound.
3. Trace the word *orange*. Circle the objects that are orange.

4.

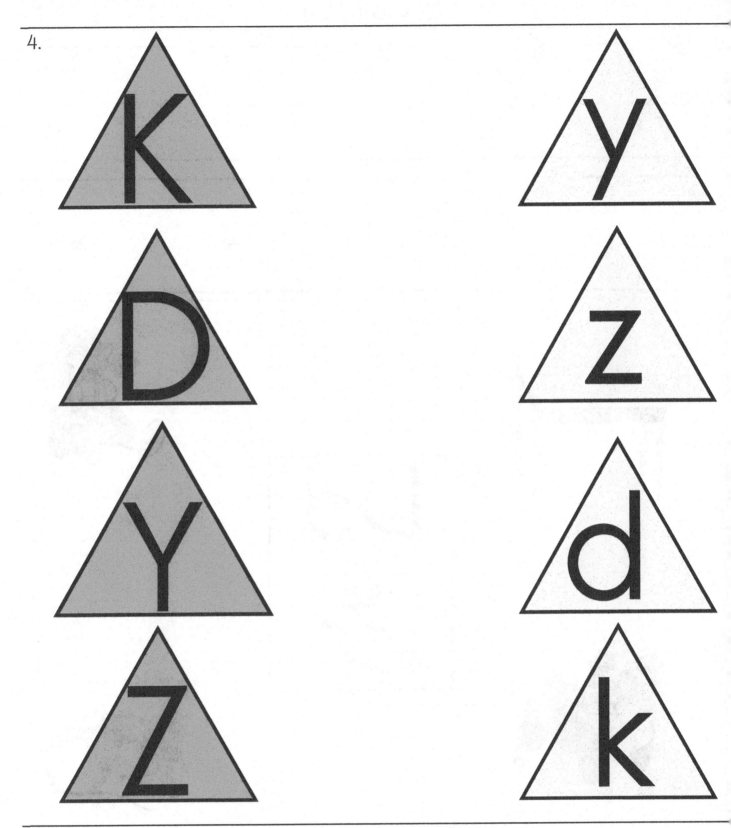

4. Draw a line to match each upper case letter to its lower case letter.

Lesson #26

1.

2.

1. Trace and write the letters.
2. Say the name of each picture. Circle the pictures that begin like *duck*.

3. Trace and write the letters.

4. Say the name of each picture. Circle the picture whose name rhymes with *cub*.

5. Circle the picture that belongs with the first one.

Lesson #27

1.

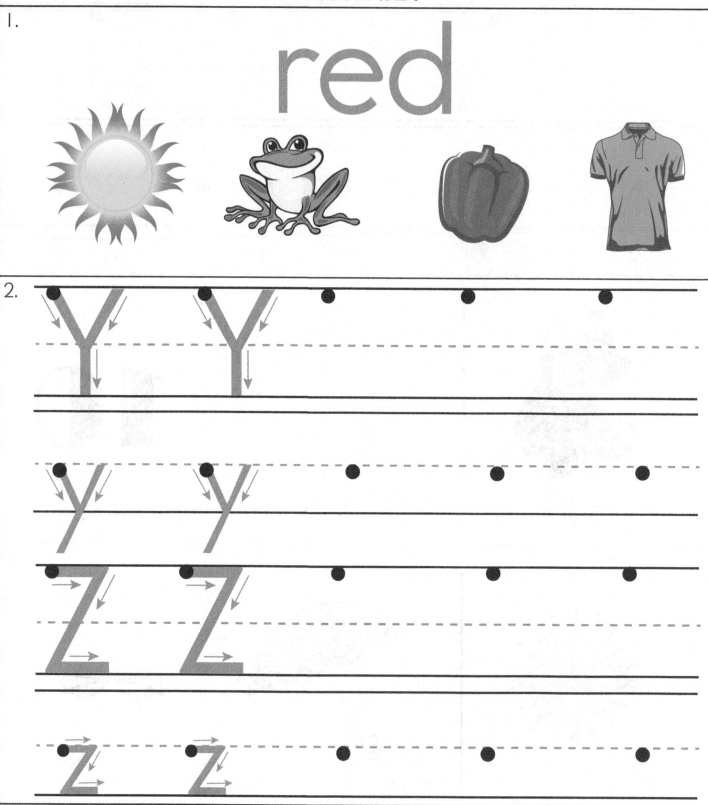

1. Trace the word *red*. Circle the objects that are red.
2. Trace and write the letters.

3.

3. Draw a line to match each upper case letter to its lower case letter.

Lesson #28

1. Say the name of each picture. Write **Ss** under the picture that begins like *seal*.

2. Circle the picture that happened last.

3. Trace and write the letters.

4.

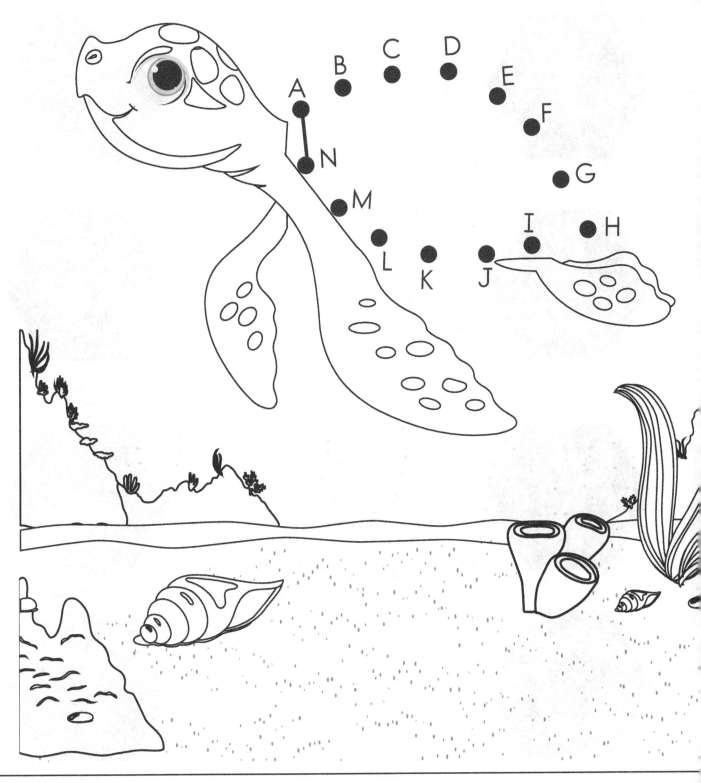

4. Connect the dots from A–N. Color the picture.

1.

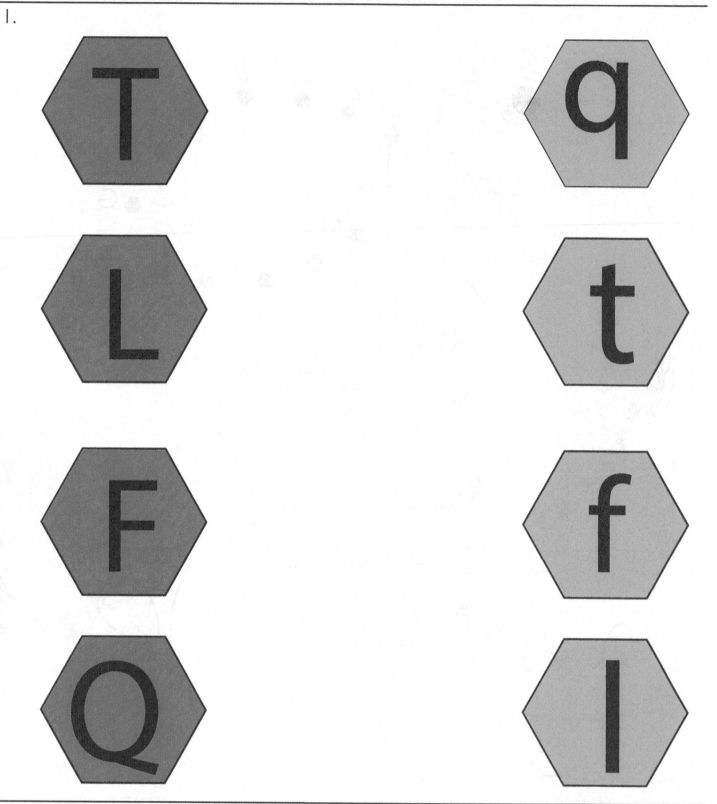

1. Draw a line to match each upper case letter to its lower case letter.

2.

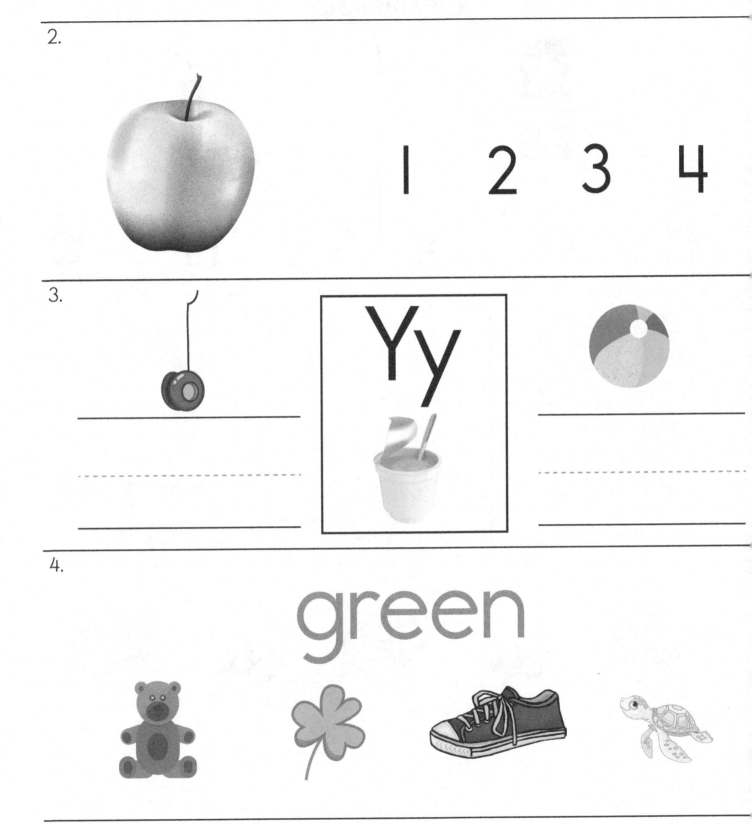

1   2   3   4

3.

Yy

4.

green

---

2. Say the word *apple*. Clap the number of beats or syllables. Circle the number of syllables.

3. Say the name of each picture. Write **Yy** under the picture that begins like *yogurt*.

4. Trace the word *green*. Circle the objects that are green.

Lesson #30

1.

g   d   x | v   n   p

2.

closed   wet   open

3.

1. Say the name of each picture. Circle the letter that stands for its beginning sound.
2. Circle the picture that shows the opposite of the first one.
3. Circle the small pinwheels.

4.

4. Read the color words. Color the hot air balloons.

Pre-K

Language Arts

Answers to Lessons

Lesson #1	Lesson #2
1.	1. B B B B B / b b b b b
2. A A A A A / a a a a a	2. D → d, F → f, A → a
3.	3. Hh
4. sad day happy	4.
	5. C C C C C / c c c c c

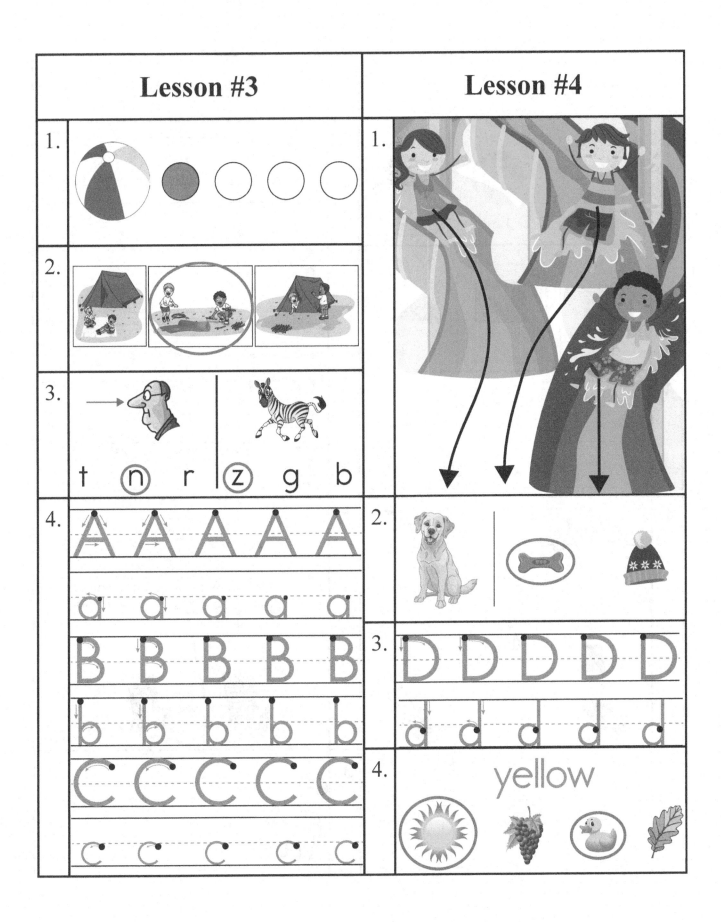

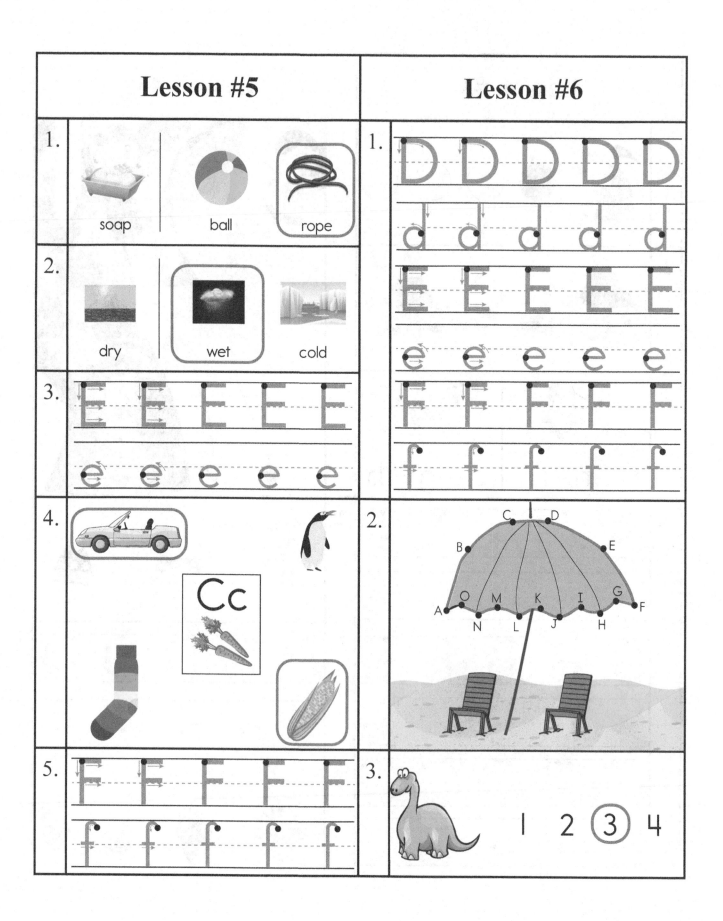

Lesson #5

1. soap | ball | rope

2. dry | wet | cold

3. E E E E E
   e e e e e

4. Cc

5. F F F F F
   f f f f f

Lesson #6

1. D D D D D
   d d d d d
   E E E E E
   e e e e e
   F F F F F
   f f f f f

2.

3. 1 2 ③ 4

Lesson #7	Lesson #8

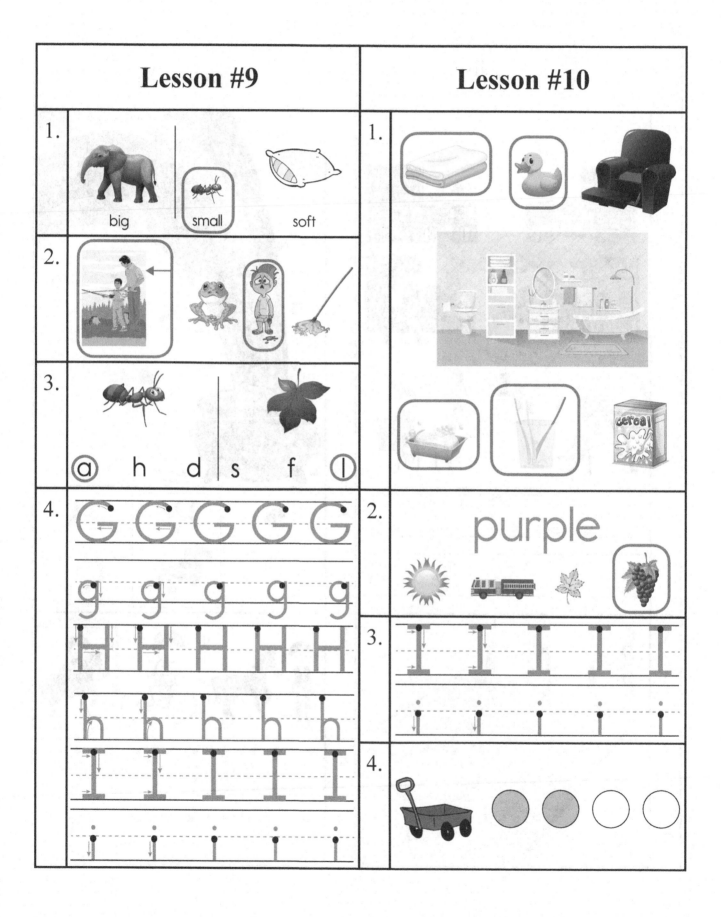

Lesson #9

1.

big   small   soft

2.

3.

(a)   h   d   s   f   (l)

4.

G G G G G

g g g g g

H H H H H

h h h h h

I I I I I

Lesson #10

1.

cereal

2.

purple

3.

I I I I I

4.

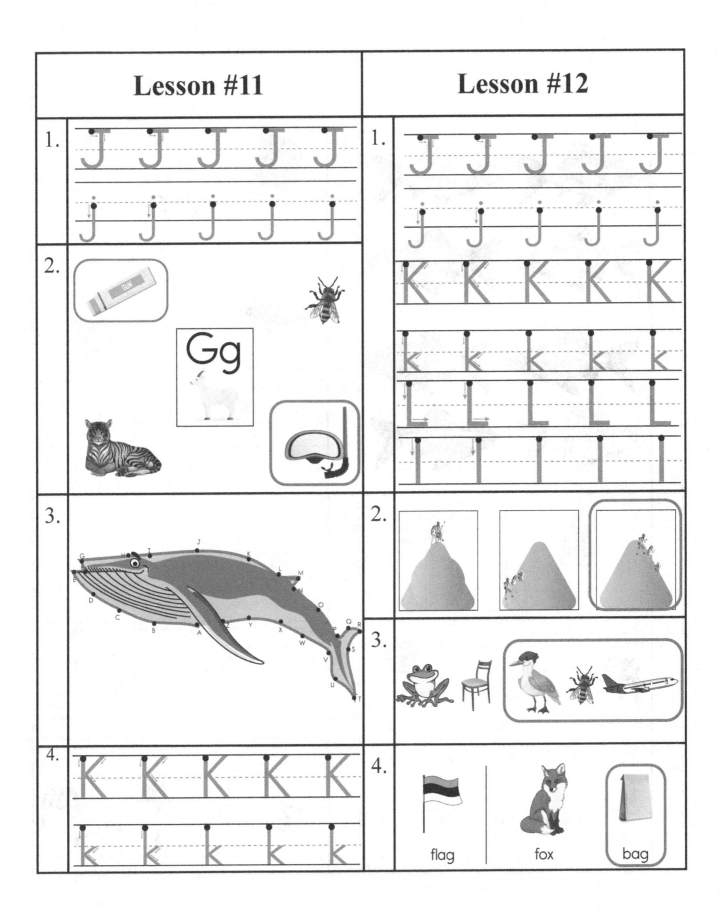

Lesson #11

1. J J J J J
   j j j j j

2. Gg

3.

4. K K K K K
   k k k k k

Lesson #12

1. J J J J J
   j j j j j
   K K K K K
   k k k k k
   L L L L L

2.

3.

4. flag   fox   bag

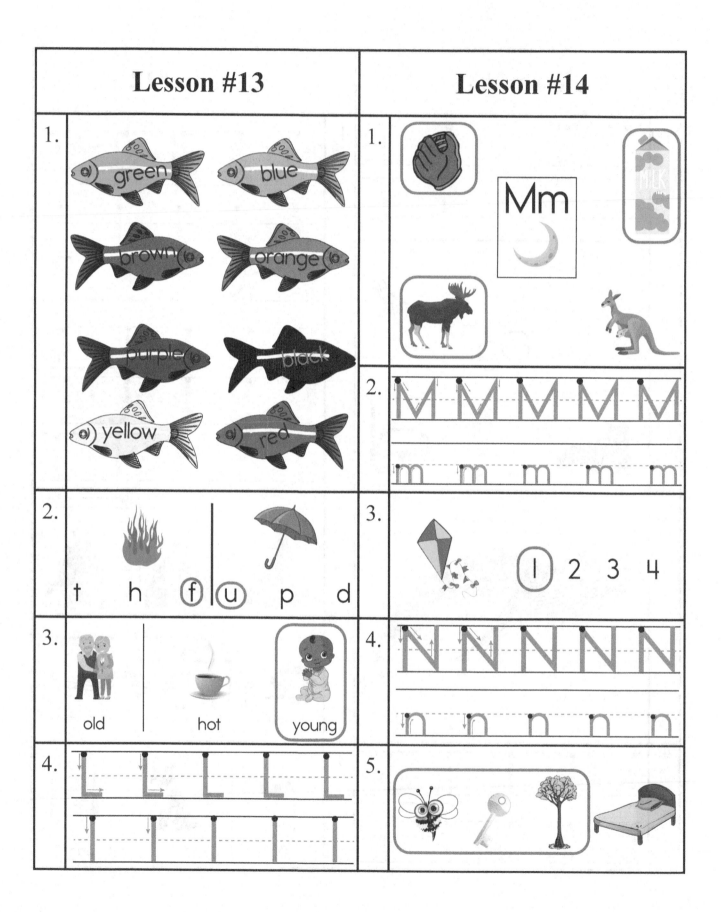

Lesson #13	Lesson #14
1. green blue brown orange purple black yellow red	1. Mm
2. t h (f) (u) p d	2. M M M M M m m m m m
3. old hot young	3. (1) 2 3 4
4. L L L L L	4. N N N N N n n n n n
	5.

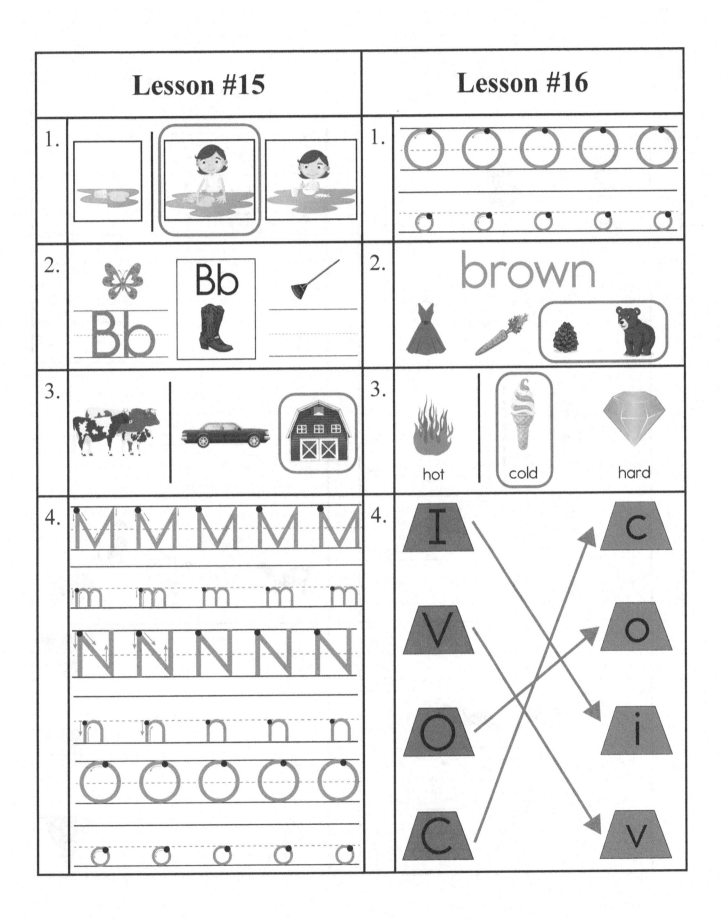

Lesson #15	Lesson #16

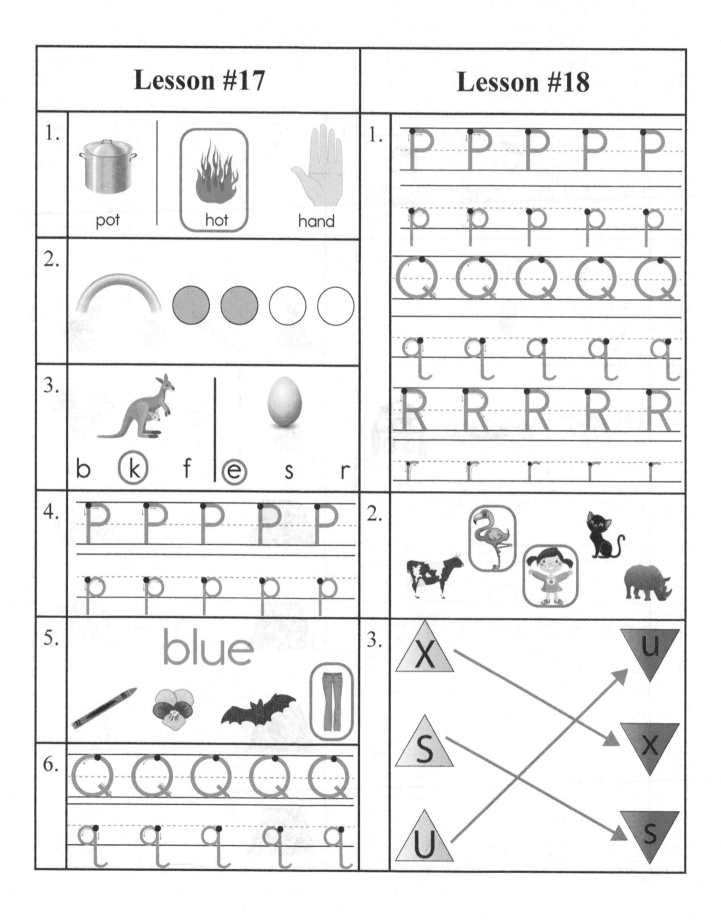

Lesson #17

1. pot | hot | hand

2.

3. b ⓚ f ⓔ s r

4. P P P P P p p p p p

5. blue

6. Q Q Q Q Q q q q q q

Lesson #18

1. P P P P P
   p p p p p
   Q Q Q Q Q
   q q q q q
   R R R R R
   r r r r r

2.

3. X → X
   S → S
   U → U

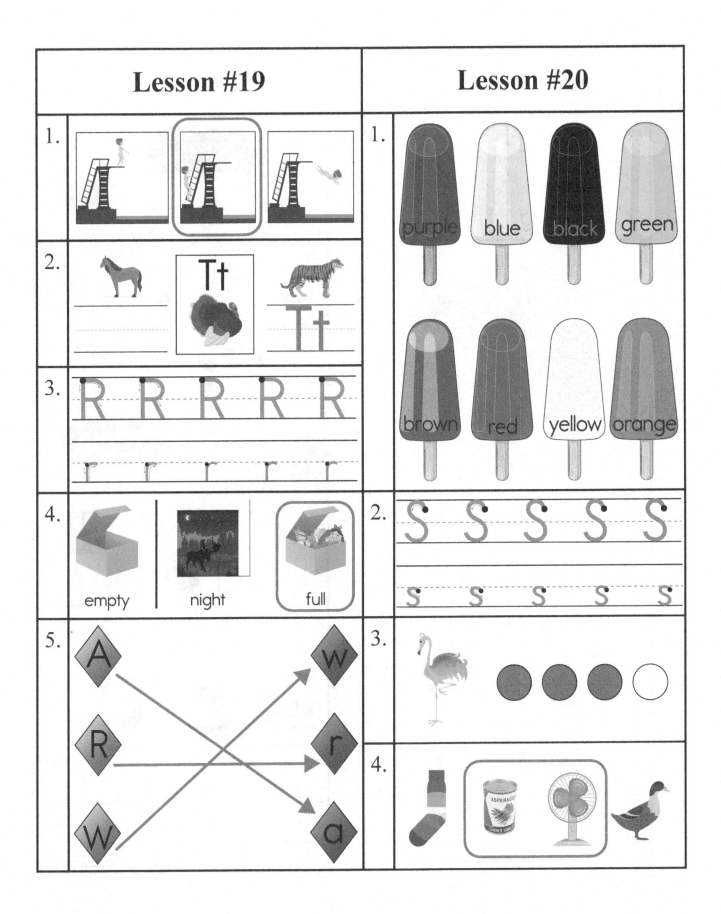

Lesson #19	Lesson #20

Lesson #19

1.

2. Tt

3. R R R R R
   r r r r r

4. empty | night | full

5. A → a
   R → r
   W → W

Lesson #20

1. purple blue black green
   brown red yellow orange

2. S S S S S
   s s s s s

3.

4.

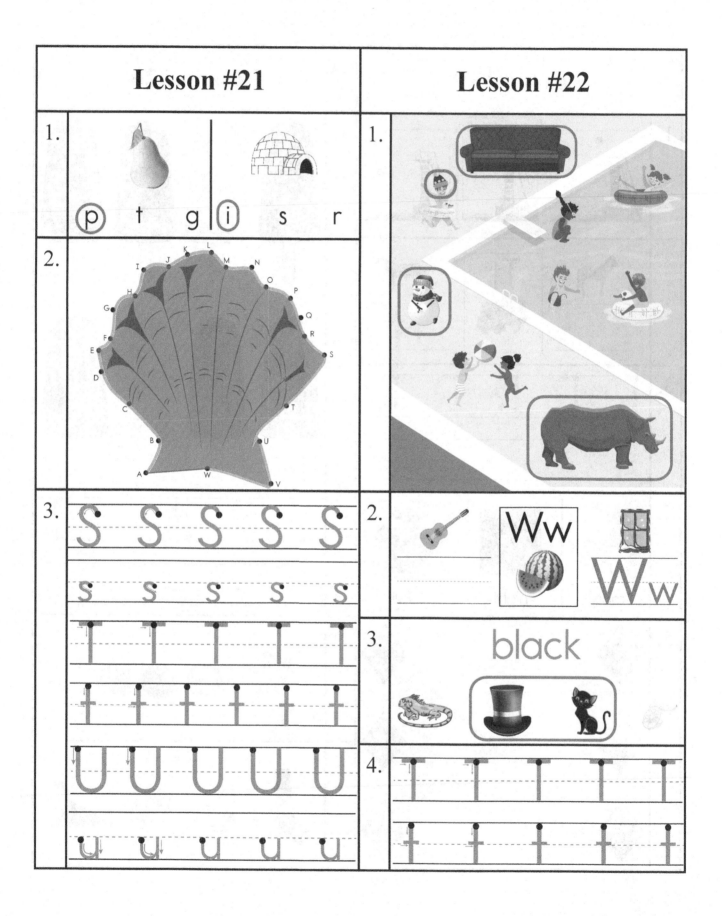

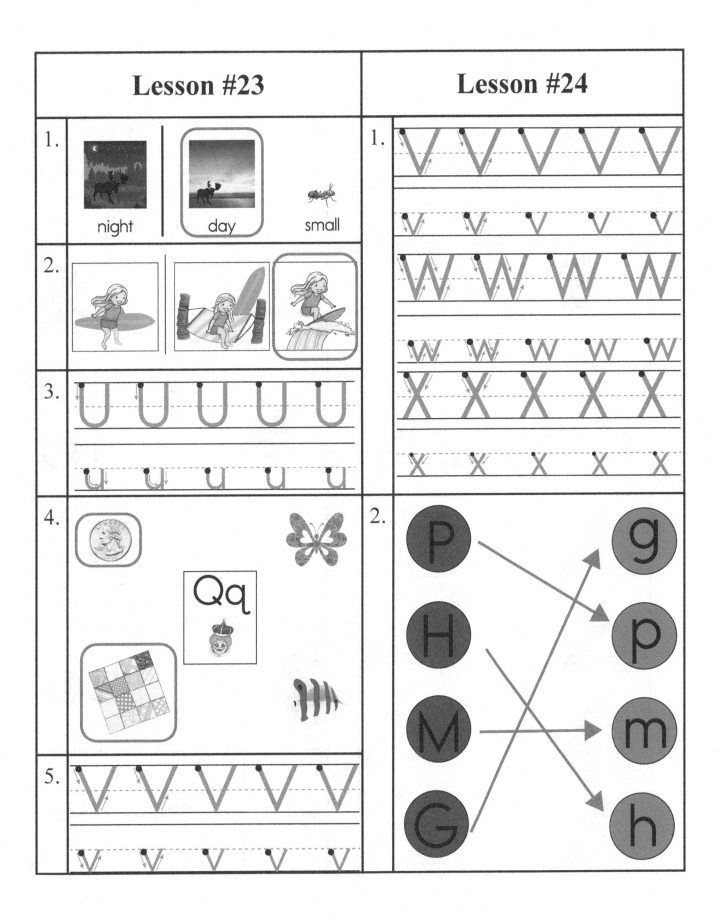

Lesson #23	Lesson #24
1. night | day small	1.
2.	
3. U u	
4. Qq	2. P H M G → g p m h
5. V v	

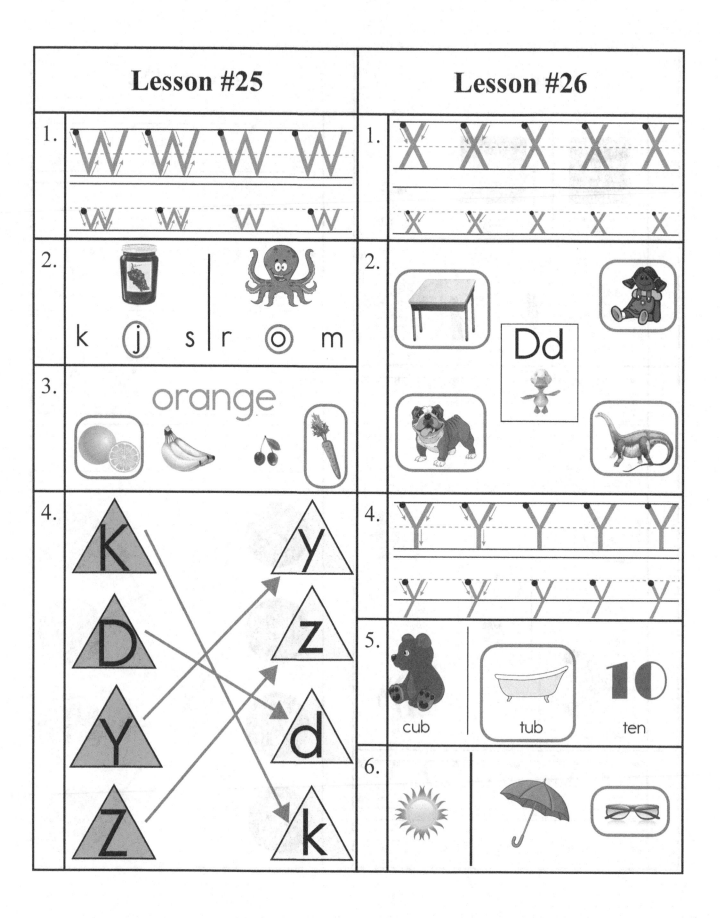

Lesson #25	Lesson #26

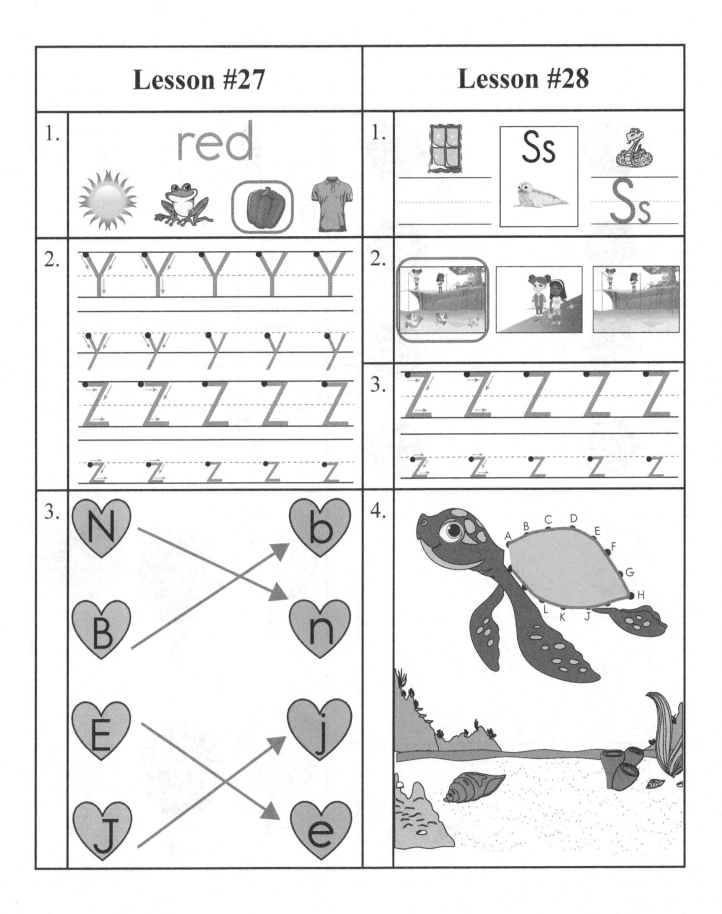

Lesson #27	Lesson #28

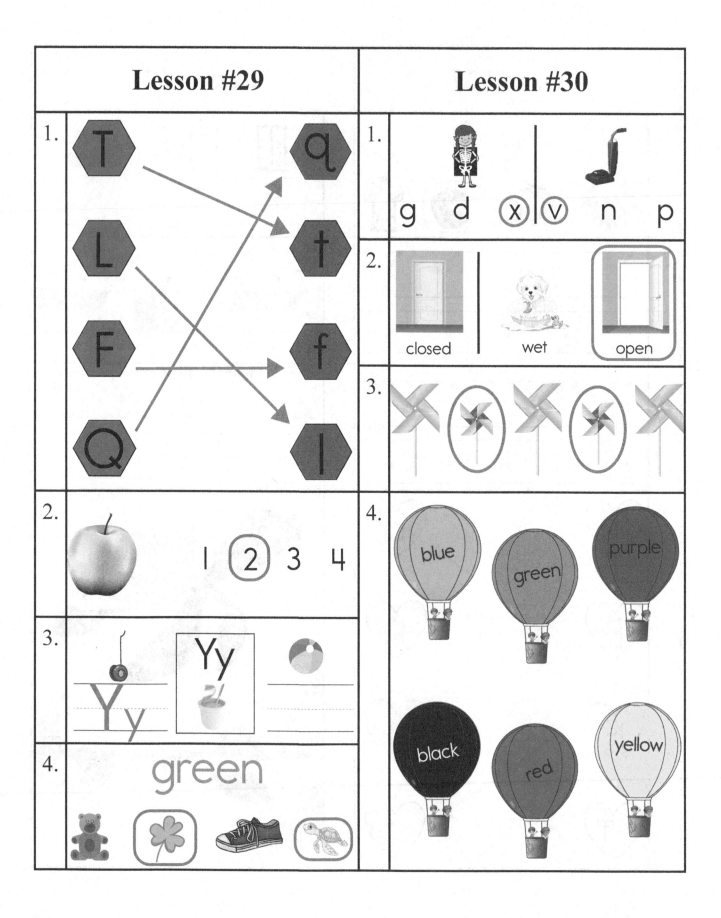

Lesson #29

1.

2.

3.

4. green

Lesson #30

1.

2.

3.

4.